This Reward Certificate for

Handwriting

is awarded to

Name

Date

Congratulations!

5+

Key Stage 1

Links school and home learning

Homework Helpers

Includes stickers and reward certificate

Handwriting

Make learning at home Fun!

Handwriting

Helpful hints for parents

- Start at the beginning of the book and try to work through the activities in order.
- Encourage your child to work independently as much as possible.
- Discuss any areas that your child finds particularly tricky and don't worry if he or she finds any of the exercises too difficult. Remember, children learn different things at different rates.
- Give help and lots of praise, rewarding your child by adding stickers to the reward certificate for great work and effort.
- Once you have completed the workbook, move on to the practice pages bound in the centre.

Autumn Publishing
www.autumnchildrensbooks.co.uk

Letter formation

Practise writing the letters of the alphabet on the lines.

a

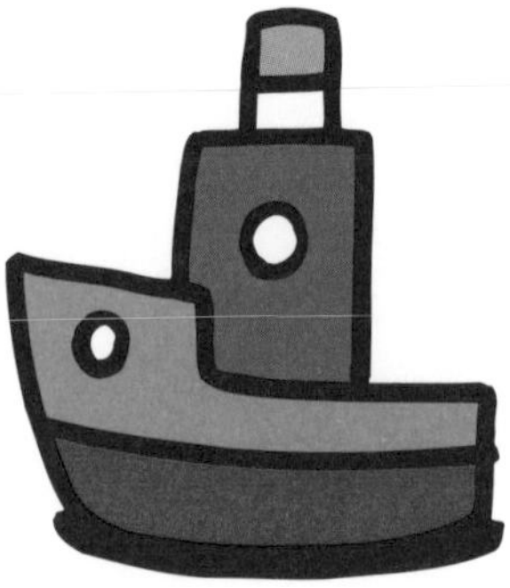

b

c

Continue writing the letters of the alphabet.

d

e

f

Letter formation

Continue writing the letters of the alphabet.

g

h

i

How many words can you think of that begin with the letters you are writing?

j

k

l

Letter formation

Continue writing the letters of the alphabet.

m

n

o

Way to go! You've almost written the entire alphabet!

p

q

r

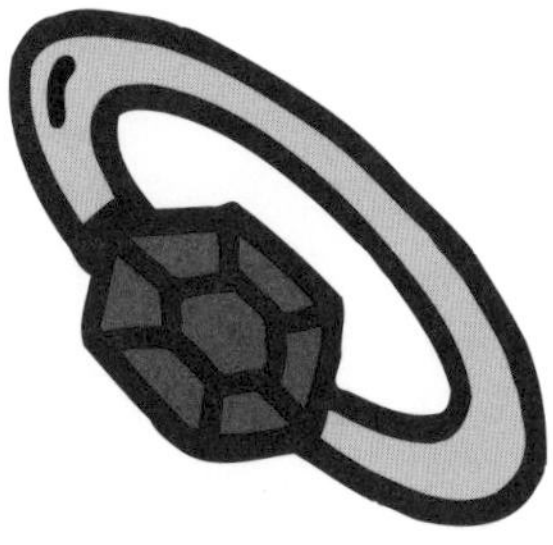

Letter formation

Continue writing the letters of the alphabet.

s

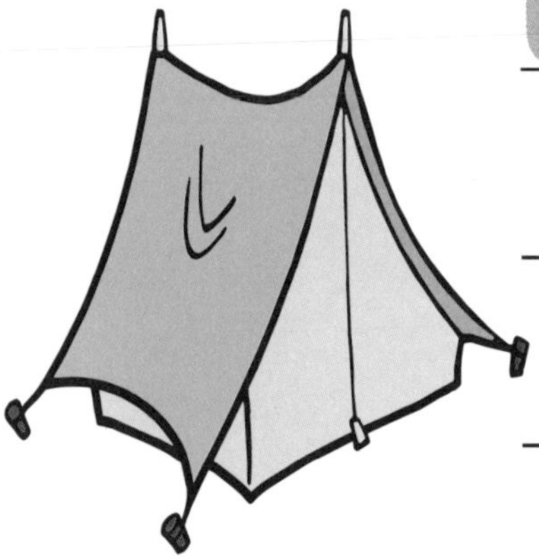

t

u

Great work! You've completed the alphabet.

v

w x

y z

Writing words

Copy these words.

shop

baby

you

cow

hair

tidy

miss

letter

What words do you already know?

train

blue

trick

flip

grow

box

how

spill

Writing words

Copy these words.

win

when

list

time

row

boy

fill

pin

Great work!

glass

pile

rain

hop

star

eat

tip

for

Writing words

Copy these words.

sand

shirt

glad

name

read

leg

pat

sun

PRACTICE MAKES PERFECT

Write the capital letters and the small letters.
Continue writing until you have filled all of the lines.

Aa Bb Cc Dd Ee Ff Gg Hh Ii Jj Kk Ll Mm
Nn Oo Pp Qq Rr Ss Tt Uu Vv Ww Xx Yy Zz

WORD COPY

**Try writing these words in your best joined-up handwriting.
Practise writing them more than once.**

anchor ______________________

butter ______________________

clown ______________________

drink ______________________

every ______________________

fun ______________________

good ______________________

hat ______________________

igloo ______________________

jam ______________________

key ______________________

lucky ______________________

mother

never

orange

pick

queen

rip

snake

train

under

vase

was

xylophone

yellow

zip

TONGUE-TWISTERS

Write these tongue-twisters in your best joined-up handwriting.

Peter Piper picked a peck of pickled peppers.

I saw Susie sitting in a shoeshine shop.

Red lorry, yellow lorry.

Around the rugged rocks, the ragged rascals ran.

Joining strokes

Some joining letters have exit strokes at their base.
Write these joining letters on the lines.

i

l

k

u

m

Joining strokes

Write these joining letters on the lines.

n

d

e

t

c

Write these joining letters on the lines.

a

d

g

o

q

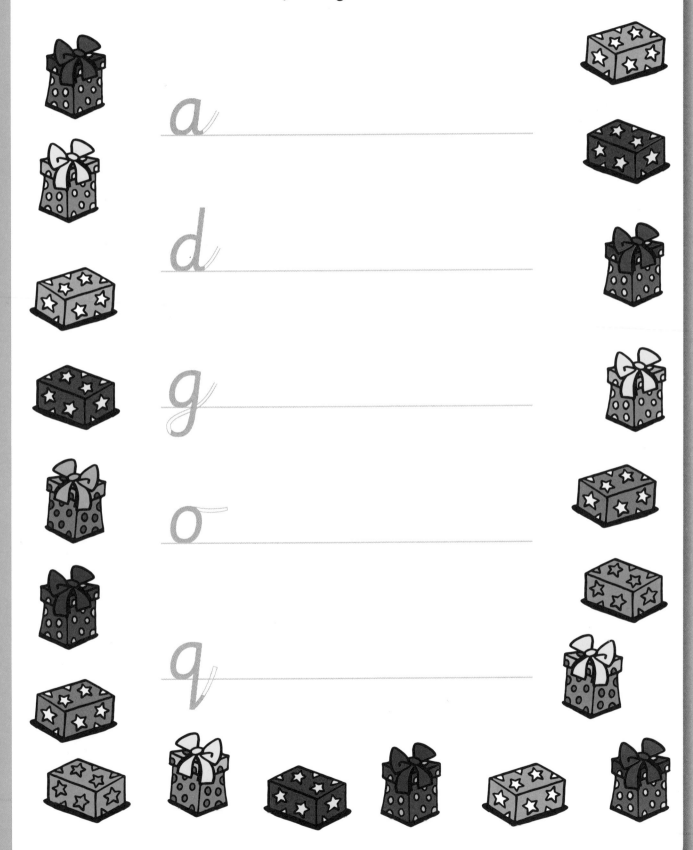

Joining strokes

Letters based on a half-circle or circle have joining strokes at the beginning. Write these joined letters on the lines.

ad

do

oc

ag

Well done!

oo

rr

vv

ww

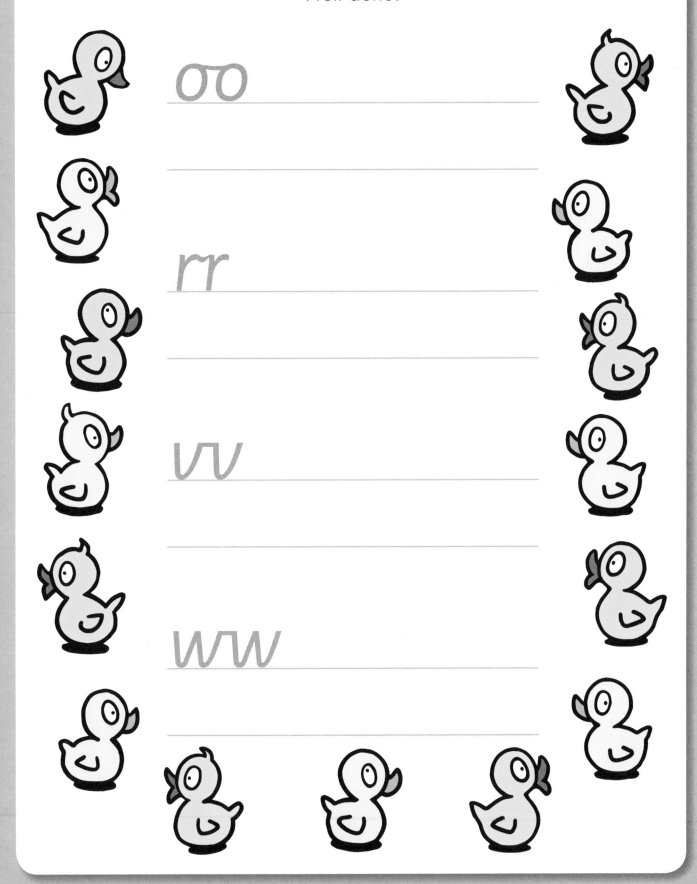

Joining strokes

Write these joined letters on the lines.

fl

fe

tu

tr

Joined-up sentences

Write these sentences using joined-up writing.

The quiet queen sat at her desk.

Parrots are colourful birds.

"Happy birthday!" they shouted.

Joined-up sentences

Write these sentences using joined-up writing.

The sausages were sizzling.

"Where are you from?" she asked.

An orderly queue had formed.

Here are some more sentences for you
to write using joined-up writing.

Zebras live in herds.

The boy shook with fright.

Her backpack was too
heavy.

Joined-up sentences

Now write these sentences using joined-up writing.

The boxes were full of clothes.

Claire liked playing the flute.

The frogs hopped to another pond.

Capital letters

Write the alphabet as capital letters.

ABCDEFG

HIJKLMN

OPQRSTU

VWXYZ

My diary

Fill in these diary details using joined-up writing.

My name is ______________________________

I like to be called _________________________

My birthday is on _________________________

My favourite colour is ____________________

I love to eat _______________________________

My friends are ____________________________

I like _____________________________________

The best thing about me is _______________

____

My address

Write your address using joined-up writing.

Address ______________________________

____

____

____

Town/city ____________________________

County ______________________________

Country _____________________________

All the letters

The sentence in the box below uses all of the letters of the alphabet at least once. Can you find them all?

The quick brown fox jumps over the lazy dog.

Write it out using joined-up writing.

Write some words of your own here in joined-up writing.
Try to use all the letters of the alphabet.

Congratulations!

You've finished the book.

Now you're ready to move on to the practice pages.

Read with Biff, Chip & Kipper

Levels 1-2

Phonics Activity Book

This book belongs to ...

....

Written by Charlotte Raby, based on the original characters created by Roderick Hunt and Alex Brychta

OXFORD
UNIVERSITY PRESS

Say the sounds, trace the letters and then write the letters.

Ss .... Bb ....

Colour in all the things that begin with **s** and **b**.

Now colour in the rest of the picture.

Can you find:

What sound do these words start with?

Say the sounds, trace the letters and then write the letters.

Aa .... Ii ....

Put the stickers on the picture. What sound do they start with?

Can you find:

What sound is in the middle of these words?

Say the sounds, trace the letters and then write the letters.

Ee Pp

Draw a line to match each letter sound with the right pictures. I spy something beginning with ...

e p

Say the sounds, trace the letters and then write the letters.

Oo .... Tt ....

Match the stickers to the letters. Say the first sound in each sticker.

o

t

What else can you think of beginning with **t**?

What can you see?

Find the stickers to finish the picture. Label the picture.

sock

cap

mug

cat

red

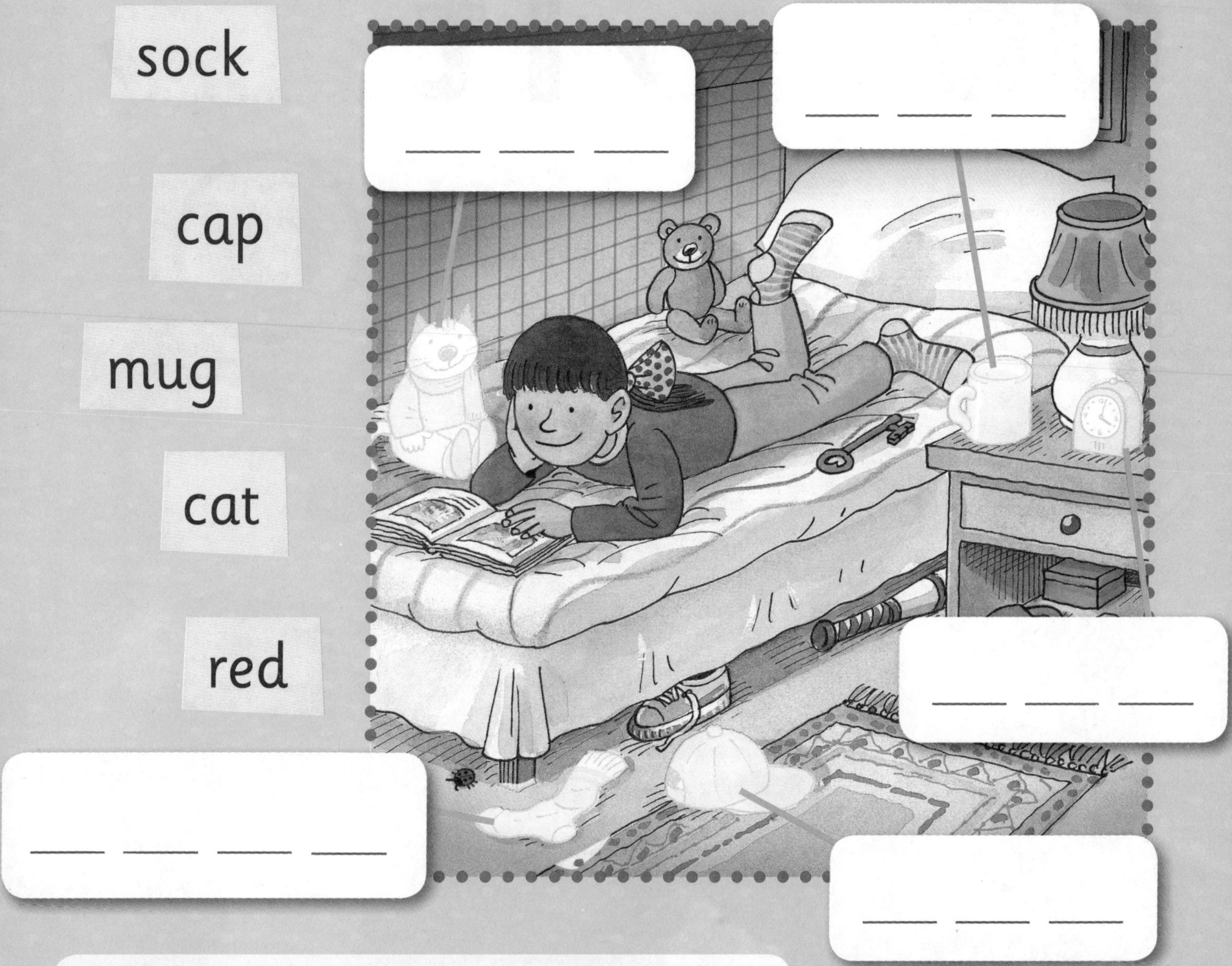

Copy this word, where is it in the picture?

bed bed ___ ___ ___

Fishing!

Follow the lines. What will they catch?

Read the letter sounds and say the
name of the picture next to it.

Some of the pictures
are missing! Can you
stick them in?

a b

c d e f

g h i j

k l m n

o p q r

s t u v

w x y z

Stickers for page 3

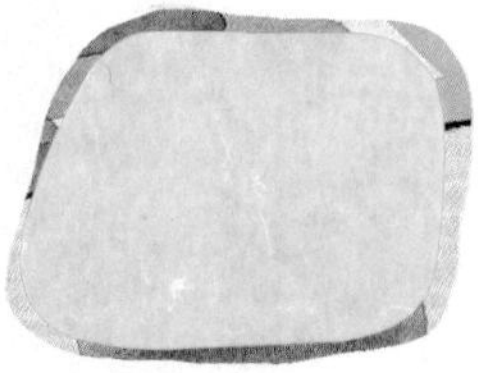

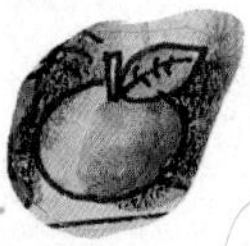

Stickers for page 5

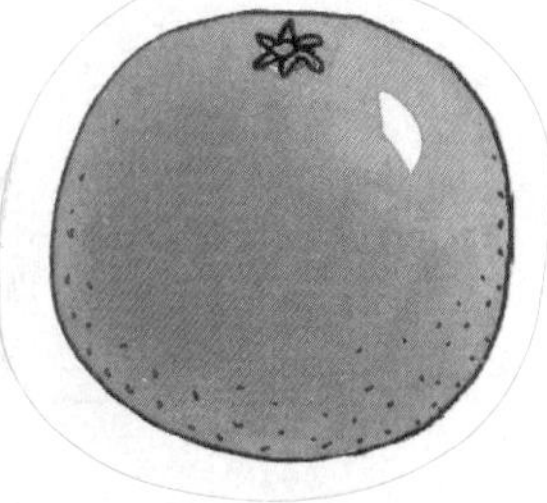

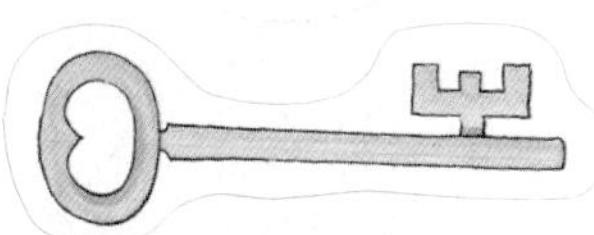
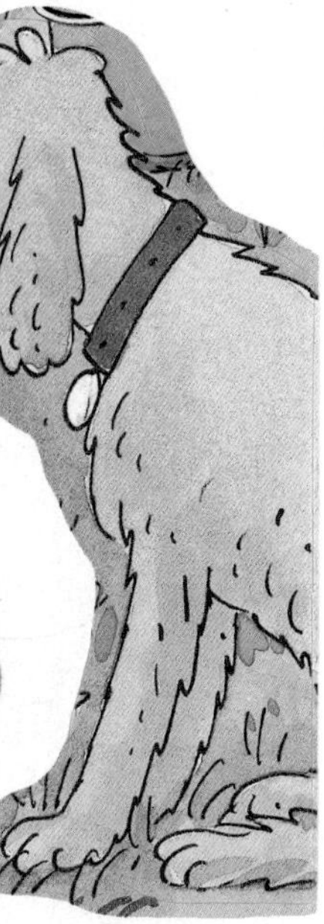

Stickers for page 8

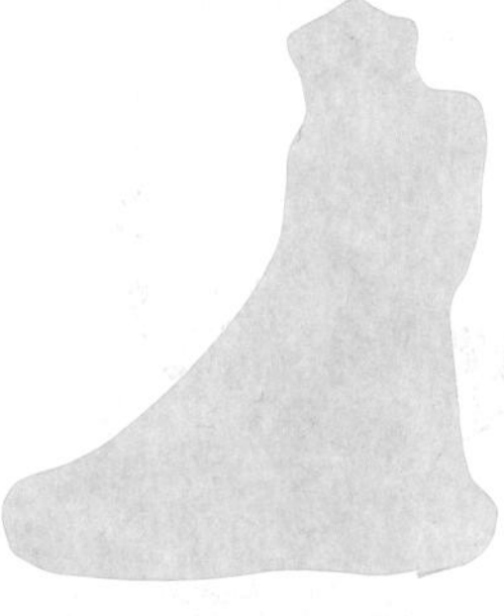

Stickers for page 15

Stickers for page 14

Stickers for page 6

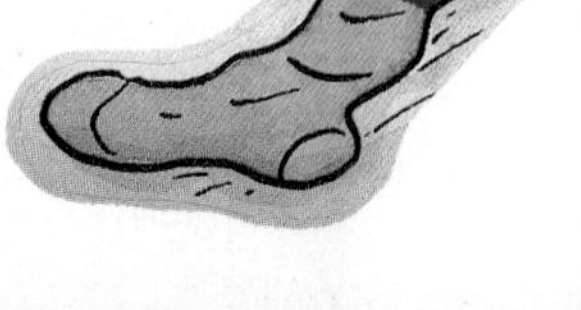

Colour by letter

Use the letters to colour in Biff.

What sound is at the beginning and at the end of **Dad**?

At the shop

Can you find these things in the picture?
Tick the things you can find.

bag ☐

cat ☐

mug ☐

till ☐

pen ☐

can ☐

hat ☐

Exploring town

Say the sounds.

a m n b u c x s

Read the words.
Can you find them
in the picture?

man

can

bus

box

Write the words.

Write the words to label the picture.

bug

Mum

mug

doll

Biff

bag

Read the words and find them in the picture. Colour in each one that you find.

log

cat

dog

mud

hat

Mum

Now colour in the rest of the picture.

Two letters, one sound

Say the sounds, trace the letters and then write the letters.

ck ....

ff ....

Read the words and find the stickers.

Biff

duck

What else can you see beginning with **d**?

What can you see?

Find the stickers to finish the picture. Label the picture.

hen

dog

Ted

bug

Read the word, trace the letters and then write the word.

cat cat ___ ___ ___

Can you find it hiding in the picture?

Alphabet dot to dot

Join the dots to finish the picture.

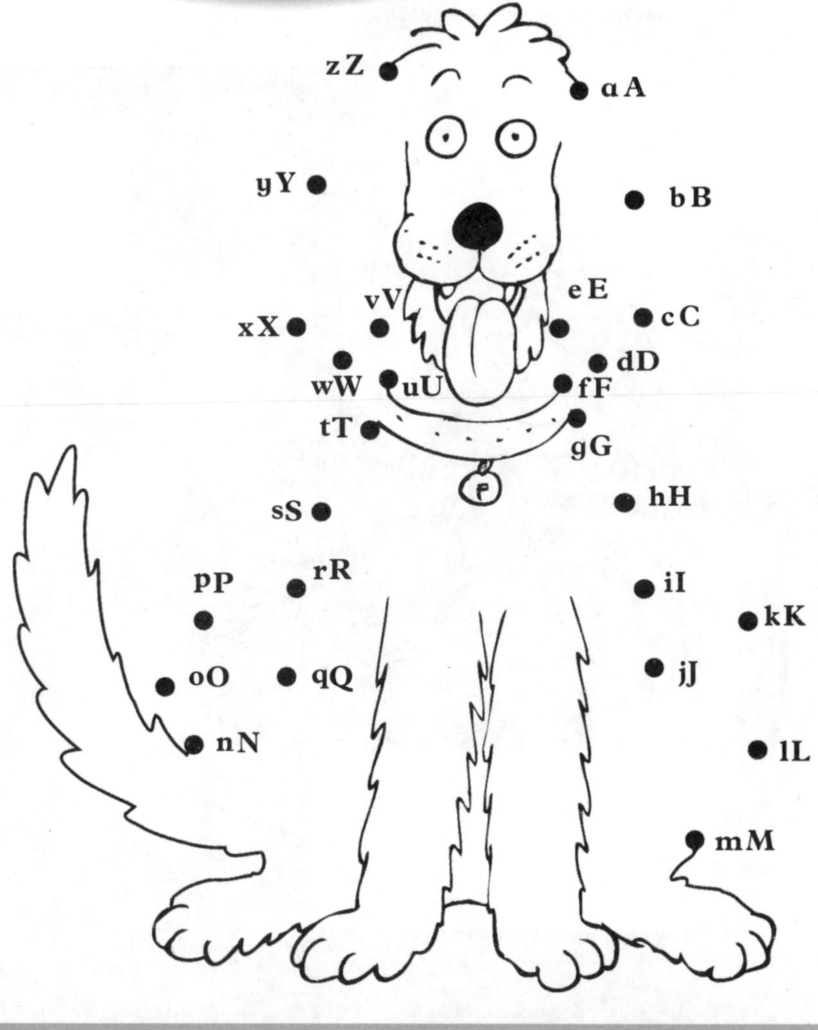

Do you know the names of these letters?
Sing the alphabet song together.